Fred Roberts
Ickleton Sunday School
Feb: 1st 1947.

THE CHILDREN'S BOOK OF SAINTS

THE INFANT ST GEORGE IS STOLEN AWAY

THE CHILDREN'S
BOOK OF SAINTS

By
F. H. LEE

Illustrated by
HONOR C. APPLETON

LONDON
GEORGE G. HARRAP & CO. LTD.
SYDNEY   TORONTO   BOMBAY   STOCKHOLM

First published January 1940
by GEORGE G. HARRAP & CO. LTD.
182 High Holborn, London, W.C.1

Reprinted: January 1941; September 1941;
August 1943; October 1945

Made in Great Britain.   Printed by Jarrold & Sons, Limited,
Norwich

CONTENTS

I

St Christopher

(ST CHRISTOPHER'S DAY: JULY 25)

LONG, long ago there lived in Greece a man called Offero, as tall and strong as a giant. He stood out from his fellows as a mighty oak does in the midst

HE STRODE OFF INTO THE FOREST

of smaller trees, and no burden seemed too heavy for him to bear.

He was poor and dwelt in a wooden hut and helped his father in the fields. He was proud of his strength, and, when about eighteen years old, he made a vow that he would search till he had found the strongest king in the world, and him he would serve.

So, taking only his staff in his hand, he strode

off into the forest, asking any he met who was the greatest king. At last he came to the court of one who seemed to be feared by all and whose armies and ships were always victorious.

When Offero asked to see the King he was received gladly, for the King was very pleased to have so powerful a helper, and for a while all went well. One day, however, a minstrel came to the palace, and as the King, arrayed in rich robes and surrounded by soldiers, listened to the minstrel's song, he turned pale and crossed himself each time the singer mentioned the name of the 'Evil One.'

"Why does he do this?" asked Offero of one of the courtiers.

"Because the Evil One is more powerful than the King, and he fears him."

"Then I must bid you farewell," said Offero to the King. "I thought you the strongest of all, but now I must seek the Evil One and serve him, since only the strongest can be my master."

So Offero set off once again, and after many days reached a wild and barren desert, where a number of gaily clad people were travelling. On a black horse at their head rode one who asked:

"Why are you here?"

"I seek the most powerful of all Kings, that I may be his servant."

"Then I am he whom thou seekest," said the stranger. "For I am the Evil One, the King of Hades."

8

"I will serve thee," said Offero, and they rode on together. Soon they came to a high place where cross-roads met, and there, by the hillside, was set up a cross on which was the figure of Christ.

As soon as the Evil One saw it he was afraid, and, turning aside, made a wide circle round to meet the roadway farther on.

"Why do you do that?" asked Offero. "Do you fear the Cross?"

But the Evil One would not answer at first, and then said, "Did you not see that on the Cross was One called Christ? He it is Who died for men, and He is the King of Heaven."

"Then He is more powerful than thou," said Offero, "and I will seek and serve Him."

Offero wandered alone far and wide, yet could not find the Christ. At length he came to a cave in the desert where lived a Holy Man, a hermit, and Offero asked him where Christ dwelt.

"Everywhere," said the hermit; "and if you would serve Him you must fast and pray."

"But if I fast I must lose my strength," said Offero, "and I know not how to pray. Bid me serve Him another way."

"Thou art noble and strong and a giant in stature," said the Hermit; "there is work thou canst do. Not far off is a swift-flowing river; many travellers and pilgrims must cross this on their way, and many are carried away by the strong waters. You can help those who come, to cross safely, and upon your shoulders you can carry the young and the

"I KNOW NOT HOW TO PRAY"

weak. Then one day your Master will most truly come to you."

"Surely this service will I do," cried Offero with joy.

He built himself a hut of logs and, with a young tree for his staff, by day and night he carried over all who came—rich and poor, old and young—so that none were ever lost. Yet the Master he served never came, and Offero grew old and bent.

Then one stormy day, not dreaming that any would seek to cross the river that day, Offero lay down in his hut and slept. Presently he was awakened by a timid knock, and a voice said, "Offero, wilt thou bear me across?"

He sprang up, but could see no one, and lay down

again. Again and yet again came the voice, and, going to the river, Offero saw a little child standing on the bank.

"What do you want so late?" he asked.

"I must cross the river to-night," answered the child; "no matter how wild the storm."

So Offero lifted the little stranger on his shoulder, and taking his staff he stepped into the water.

The waves rose and the strong current almost carried him away, and, as he struggled on, the child seemed to grow heavier and heavier; the storm became more terrible, and it took all his strength to reach the other side.

"I never carried so great a burden before," he said, putting the child down gently. "Whom have

IT TOOK ALL HIS STRENGTH TO REACH THE OTHER SIDE

I carried this night? Had it been the whole world it could not have been heavier."

Suddenly the storm ceased, and the child said, "You have indeed borne the world on your shoulders, for you have borne Him who made it. I am Jesus Christ, the King whom you have served at this river. You shall no longer be called Offero, but Christopher, the Christ-Bearer; and that you may know my words are true, put your staff into the ground, and flowers and fruit will grow on it."

And as Christopher watched, his staff put forth fresh leaves and fruit, the Christ-Child vanished, and he was left alone. St Christopher had indeed found the greatest of all Kings, and when his work on earth was ended, he went to dwell in the Kingdom of God above.

II

St Nicholas

THREE hundred years after Christ lived, a baby boy called Nicholas was born in Patara, in Lycia. His parents were very rich and were very happy at his birth.

Suddenly, as he was being bathed, the new-born babe stood up, and clasping his hands together, he raised his eyes to Heaven. For two hours he stayed thus as if in prayer, while those around feared to touch him, knowing that he must be a Holy Child.

As the days passed, their wonder grew, for on each Friday and fast day the tiny child refused to take even one drop of milk, and people marvelled that one so young should know the Holy Days.

His parents died when Nicholas was a young man, and he was then very rich. Yet he cared nothing for money, and, vowing he would use his wealth to help the poor and needy, he became a monk in a monastery near by.

Now in Patara there lived a poor nobleman who had lost all his money, and he and his three daughters were like to starve. Nor could he ever provide a marriage dower or gift for them, and without this no one would wed them. Sad and troubled, he could think of no other way than to take them to the market the next day and sell them as slaves to rich men.

When Nicholas heard of their distress he went secretly to the house at night, and, as the nobleman sat alone and sorrowful, Nicholas dropped a bag of gold through the open window.

The nobleman was amazed and stooped to pick it up. He could see no one near, but his heart rejoiced that now his eldest daughter would have a wedding dowry, and the next day she and her lover made their vows to each other and thanked Heaven for their unknown friend.

The next night the nobleman sat thinking of his other two daughters who must surely be sold, when suddenly a second and a larger bag of gold was dropped in at the open window. Again St Nicholas was gone before the nobleman could reach the door, and on the morrow the second daughter and her lover also made their vows to each other and thanked Heaven for their unknown friend.

The nobleman now made up his mind to keep watch, so he stole out and hid himself near the house. As soon as the sun went down he heard the sound of hurried footsteps, and St Nicholas passed by, dropping a third bag of gold into the open window.

Running quickly from his hiding-place, the nobleman seized Nicholas by his robe and cried, "Oh, Nicholas, servant of God, why seek you to hide yourself?"

"That is my way of making others happy,"

replied Nicholas, "and I pray you not to tell anyone of it, not even your daughters."

The nobleman promised, and the third daughter was betrothed to her lover. But somehow the secret was told and written down for all to read.

"WHY SEEK YOU TO HIDE YOURSELF?"

After this Nicholas started on a pilgrimage to the Holy Land. As the ship set sail a great storm came on. The sailors toiled in vain, for the waves rose mountains high, and the ship seemed like to break in two.

Suddenly the sailors saw Nicholas kneeling in prayer upon the deck, and as he prayed, the sea began to grow calm, and the ship was saved and reached the harbour in time.

"Truly," said the Captain, "from this time onward whenever sailors are in danger let them call upon the name of Nicholas, who will be the patron saint of seamen everywhere."

During his pilgrimage to the Holy Land, St Nicholas went barefooted and bareheaded, that he might be humble in places where Christ Himself had trod, and on his return he was made Bishop of Myra.

Soon after this a famine spread over the land, and the people were desperate with hunger. Nicholas could do nothing but pray; then there came to him a dream in which he saw three ships laden with corn for Alexandria, and a voice said, "Go! Buy food for the people."

Awaking from sleep, he found three pieces of gold beside his bed, and going at once to the harbour, he saw the ships and asked to buy the corn.

"Nay, Father," said the sailors, "this wheat is for the Emperor, and we dare not sell even one measure full."

"But," said Nicholas, "if you do as I ask, God will not allow your store to be less."

So they sold corn to Nicholas, who was able not only to feed his people, but to have seeds for sowing in his fields for future days.

One night on his travels St Nicholas came to an inn, and being tired and hungry, he asked for food and shelter there. The innkeeper bade him come in and gladly set about preparing a meal of pickled meat for his guest. When, however, Nicholas looked at the food, he turned sharply to the innkeeper, saying, "Where is the rest of this pickled pork?"

"It is in the tub over there," answered the innkeeper, beginning to be uneasy.

At this Nicholas crossed over to the tub, then lifting his eyes to heaven, he made the sign of the Cross over it. As he did so there rose from the strange tub the beautiful forms of three little boys whom the innkeeper had cruelly slain and pickled.

On finding his evil ways discovered, the innkeeper begged for mercy, and St Nicholas, having restored the now happy children to their mother, prayed that God would forgive the man's sins.

No wonder Nicholas became ever afterwards the guardian saint of little children, and his feast-day is always a time of gladness for them, for does he not come while they are asleep and fill their little stockings or shoes with gifts, and hasten off that no one may ever see him?

III
St George
(St George's Day : April 23)

VERY long ago in a lonely cave near Coventry dwelt a Wise Lady of the Woods. She was a wicked enchantress, who by her cunning had stolen away the new-born son of Lord Albert of Coventry, and carried him off to her cave.

There she kept him for many years, and though she hated all that was good and noble, she had a great love for the child George, and wanted him to become a powerful knight. So he was taught all that a knight should know; but he was not happy and longed to ride away and do great deeds, though he did not tell the Wise Lady of the Woods of this, for she wanted to keep him with her always.

One day she took him to a castle of brass, and having told him who he really was, she gave him a wonderful horse, Bayard, a splendid suit of armour, and, best of all, a magic sword, Ascalon, which would never fail him.

St George was now all the more eager to escape from the witch's power, and at the first chance, with the help of her own magic wand, he imprisoned her in a great rock and rode hastily away on his adventures.

His journeys led him at last to the land of Egypt,

and, being weary, he asked shelter for the night from a hermit who lived in a small hut by the wayside.

"You may rest here, and welcome," answered the hermit. And St George entered.

HE RODE HASTILY AWAY ON HIS ADVENTURES

After laying aside his armour, he noticed how downcast the hermit seemed, and said, "Why are you so sad, Holy Father?"

"Good reason have we to be troubled," replied the hermit. "And sad indeed is my story.

"In yonder town of Silene there is great distress, for in the dark waters of a lake near by dwells a terrible dragon. Its scales are as hard as brass, its wings are like flames, its front paws are as strong as a lion, in its jaws are teeth of iron, while from its nostrils comes thick poisonous smoke.

"Soldiers have been sent to kill it, but are driven back by its fiery breath. Indeed, all ways of destroying it have been tried in vain.

19

"Each day for years the fearsome creature crawls swiftly across the marshy land towards the town, and each day two sheep have been sent out from the gates to feed the monster. These it has devoured greedily and then disappeared into the lake again.

A TERRIBLE DRAGON

"At last, when all the sheep and cattle were gone, the King assembled his people and said, 'We have nothing now left to give this cruel dragon, save ourselves; for if we do not provide a meal the whole town will be destroyed by its breath.'

"So each morning they cast lots, and he on whom the lot fell went forth from the gates alone. And now the King is in sore trouble, for the lot has this day fallen upon his own daughter, the beautiful princess Sabra, and to-morrow she must be led forth. Pity, indeed, is it that one so fair and so beloved should meet so cruel a death."

"Let me but rest awhile," said St George; "then show me the valley where the dragon comes, and I will fight the monster."

The next morning the princess dressed herself in her best robe and, bidding farewell to her father and the people, she went forth bravely and alone from the gates.

As she drew near to the dreaded place her heart failed her, and she sat down and wept for sorrow

AS SHE DREW NEAR TO THE DREADED PLACE HER HEART
FAILED HER

and fear. So dim were her eyes with tears that she did not see that some one was approaching.

Suddenly there was the sound of hoofs and, looking up, she beheld a knight in shining armour on a white charger coming towards her.

"Why do you weep, fair maid?" he asked. And she told him of the fearsome monster that was even then on its way.

"Fear not, gentle maid," said St George; "for by the help of God I will slay the dragon and free all your people from its power."

Quickly he lifted the princess on to his horse and took her to a place of safety. Then, turning once more towards the marsh, he saw the dragon approaching. It rushed straight towards him, making a noise like thunder and sending out fiery breath.

St George charged at it, but his spear glanced off the creature's back. Again and again he struck, but no wound could he make.

Then he and his horse were felled to the ground, but as the dragon raised itself over him, the knight drove his spear under its wing and wounded it.

The fight was by no means over, however; for hours they struggled, and at last St George thrust his sword into the dragon's mouth, and the creature fell dead at his feet.

The King and his people, thinking that the princess had been devoured, mourned her death, when suddenly they heard a great shout and, rushing to the watch-towers, they were amazed to see their own princess alive and safe, and by her side an unknown knight dragging the lifeless body of the dragon.

At first they feared to open the gates, but when St George cried, "The dragon is dead," they were almost beside themselves with joy and threw them open to welcome their deliverer and their princess.

So ended the fight of St George and the dragon. Many more adventures he had and many enemies to overcome, yet he was always ready to protect the weak and to be the champion of the helpless.

He suffered many hardships, and for seven years was imprisoned for the sake of the beautiful princess Sabra, but at last he was able to take her with him to England, where they were married and great joy was theirs to the end.

IV

St Jerome

St Jerome was born in the year 346 at Stridon, on the shores of the Adriatic Sea. His parents were both Christians, and Jerome was taught at first by his mother and father, but afterwards went to Rome. There he lived rather a gay life and was a great favourite with his friends.

After a time, however, he began to grow tired of the chariot-races and the playhouse and such pleasures, and settled down to study.

He searched for old writings and began to write out parts of the Old Testament in Latin.

Later he journeyed to the East and lived for five years as a priest in the desert, where he employed his time in prayer and writing and making mats. He even made a garden there, by no means an easy thing in the desert.

When he returned to Rome, many important people came to him for his blessing, and among his best friends was the Lady Paula, who, with her daughters, afterwards went on a pilgrimage to Bethlehem. There she built four convents, over which Jerome ruled for thirty-four years.

One day, as he sat with the monks near the gateway of the monastery, they were amazed to see

a lion coming towards them. The monks jumped
up and fled in fear; Jerome, however, waited calmly.
The lion looked at Jerome, then held up a swollen
paw as if asking the saint to cure it. Jerome held

HELD UP A SWOLLEN PAW

the paw and, seeing a large thorn in the soft part
underneath, pulled it gently out.

"Surely that is better," he said to the lion. "Now
come to my cell, and I will bathe it with healing
herbs and bandage it, too."

When this was done Jerome tried to make the
lion go away, but instead it settled down at his feet
and seemed to say, "I mean to stay here always."

25

So Jerome went to bed, and the lion lay on the floor beside him. The next morning Jerome again tried to drive his strange visitor away, but the grateful creature followed him quietly everywhere.

"Well," said Jerome, "if you stay here you must work; no one can be idle. Every day you must go with my donkey into the forest and, while the logs for firewood are being piled into its panniers, you must guard it from all harm from robbers and wild beasts. See, I trust you to look after the donkey."

The lion wagged its tail and held up the wounded paw to show it was ready to work, and the two creatures set off side by side. Then, while the old man loaded up the panniers with logs, the lion kept guard, and each evening the firewood was brought safely home.

One day, however, the lion grew very drowsy with the heat, and before long was fast asleep. Many hours it slept, and when it awoke the dawn was breaking. It yawned and stretched itself, then looked round for the donkey. Nowhere could it be seen; the old man was gone, too.

The lion searched everywhere, then seeing human footprints on the ground, it said to itself, "Alas, I have been unfaithful; the donkey must have been stolen by robbers while I slept."

So, hanging its head with shame and with its tail between its legs, the lion went back to the monastery.

Here St Jerome met him, and the lion at once

crouched down at his master's feet as if begging to be forgiven.

"Where is the donkey?" asked the saint sternly. "I trusted you to take care of it. You must have

HANGING ITS HEAD WITH SHAME AND WITH ITS TAIL
BETWEEN ITS LEGS

eaten it. You must therefore do its work, and carry home the firewood logs on your back."

The lion wagged its tail as if to say it wanted to help, and each day it journeyed into the forest. Then one day a caravan was seen coming over the hills on its way to Egypt. There were camels laden with silks and other things, and men and horses, and at the head of the line was a donkey.

Suddenly the lion lifted its head, stood still for an instant, then, with a glad roar, it bounded forward towards the caravan, upsetting the logs and the old man too.

The camel-drivers fled in alarm, and the lion drove the merchants and camels and the donkey into the monastery yard. There was great confusion, but when Jerome saw the donkey he understood what had happened, while the lion seemed beside itself with joy.

Throwing themselves before the saint, the merchants confessed that they had stolen the donkey on the day the lion had slept.

"We pray thee to forgive us this wrong," they said. And Jerome, in the kindness of his heart, bade them go in peace.

So the lion and donkey once more went out each day to the forest for firewood, and in the evening the lion would crouch at the saint's feet as he wrote in his cell. Not even in death did the faithful creature leave Jerome, but lay upon the grave of its loved master till it died of grief.

IT LAY UPON THE GRAVE OF ITS LOVED MASTER

V

St Patrick

HUNDREDS of years ago, on a farm near the sea-coast in Gaul, lived a young lad called Patrick. His parents were Christians, and he loved them dearly, but he did not care as much for the church as they did, and was happier away on the hillside.

When he was about sixteen some pirate Kings of the Picts and Scots landed upon the shore near his home, and, seizing Patrick and other lads, carried them off as prisoners to Ireland. There Patrick was sold as a slave to King Milcho of Dalriada, who sent him to the dreary Slemish Mountain to feed pigs.

In his loneliness and sorrow he thought much about his mother and her prayers, and he too learned to know God, rising even before dawn each day to worship and to pray that he might one day be free.

For seven years he served as a swineherd, then one night in a dream he heard a voice say, "You have prayed and fasted well; you shall go back to your own country."

When he awoke he wondered how he could ever escape. Then a second message came, "The ship is ready, go to the shore."

29

FOR SEVEN YEARS HE SERVED AS A SWINEHERD

Feeling certain that this was the voice of God and that he was to be set free, he hastened away towards the coast, which was many miles distant. There he found a ship, and going to the Captain, he said, "I want to go to France."

"Have you any money?" asked the Captain.

"I have none, but I will work and repay you when I reach France," answered Patrick.

"Be off," said the Captain roughly.

But Patrick prayed that God would help him, and when he had gone but a short distance, the sailors called him back and said he might sail with them.

In three days they reached Brittany, and after a

dangerous journey through a forest, nearly dying of hunger on the way, Patrick found his old home.

There he was gladly received, but he could not rest long, for he wanted to be a priest; so he went on to his uncle, St Martin of Tours, where he lived for three years in a cave by the riverside.

While he journeyed about the countryside his thoughts dwelt much on Ireland, and one night an angel, holding out a letter, came to him in a vision. Patrick read the words on it—"The Voice of the Irish"—and then it seemed that voices came as if from a wood, chanting, "Oh! Holy Boy, come and walk again among us."

When he awoke Patrick knew that it was the call of the children of Ireland, yet to be born; and that during the next few years he must prepare himself for the work. In time he became a Bishop and then set sail once more for the wild Irish coast.

When he and his friends landed, the herdsmen on the hills thought they must be robbers, and ran to tell their master Dichu, who came quickly out of his barn ready to fight the intruders.

Then Patrick cried, "I was a slave in this land, but am now free. You have lived too long in fear of the Druids, and I have come to set you free from their power."

Dichu listened to all Patrick had to say, and after some time he decided to be baptized and be a Christian. He also gave the barn to Patrick as a home, and there the Saint's first Mass in Ireland was said.

From this time many wonderful works of healing and help were performed by Patrick, and everywhere people talked of his power and many believed his words and were baptized.

But the power of the Druids was still very strong, and at Easter-time they held a great spring festival. Laeghaire, King of Ireland, dwelt in a castle on the Hill of Tara, and here princes and bards and Druids were gathered together, waiting anxiously for the great ceremony of lighting the Druid flame, sacred to the spring.

All fires had been put out, and, at a special time, the Druid's fire was to be lit on Tara's Hill, after which other fires might be lit on the hills around.

Now Patrick longed to show the King and his men that they ought rather to worship the risen Christ, so he went with the men who believed in him to the Hill of Slane, ten miles away.

There he made ready a Holy Fire, sacred to God, and waited till nightfall, when all was in darkness. Then he lit the Sacred Fire.

Suddenly the King was astonished to see the strange flames upon the Hill of Slane.

"Who has dared to disobey my law?" he cried. And the Druids answered in fear, "O King, unless this fire be put out this very night, he who has lit it shall overcome us all."

Then in all haste the King and his people and Druids hastened towards the flame and would have killed Patrick; but he had no fear and stood before them and sang, "Let God arise and let his enemies be scattered."

HE LIT THE SACRED FIRE

A strange darkness then spread over the land, and the King's men fled in terror, many being killed in the confusion. But the King remained firm, and when the tumult had died down, it was agreed that

Patrick should go to Tara Hall the next day to tell them about the risen Christ.

Now the King still had it in mind to destroy Patrick, and men were sent to lie in ambush for him on the journey. But they only saw a few deer and a young fawn with a bird upon its back pass by in the mist, so they returned to Tara's Hall disappointed.

Yet in very truth the deer were Patrick and his followers, and the little fawn was the child Benignus, Patrick's first friend and servant, carrying his master's books upon his back.

While they walked, Patrick, knowing the King's hatred, composed this beautiful hymn to sing:

> I bind to myself this day
> The Power of God to guide me,
> The might of God to uphold me,
> The wisdom of God to teach me,
> The eye of God to watch over me,
> The ear of God to hear me,
> The word of God to give me speech,
> The hand of God to protect me,
> The way of God to lie before me,
> The shield of God to guard me,
> The hosts of God to defend me.
>
> Christ be with me and before me,
> Christ be behind me and within me,
> Christ be below me and above me,
> Christ at my right hand and my left.

His prayers were answered, and they were saved from the King's men; and when poisoned wine

34

was poured into his cup at the banquet, Patrick made the Sign of the Cross over it and it became harmless. Such wonders did he perform that the King at last said that St Patrick's God should be his God, and he became a Christian.

Patrick travelled through the land preaching, baptizing, and founding churches, and everywhere people flocked to hear him.

THE EMBLEM OF
ST PATRICK

One day, wishing to explain that in God there were three persons— the Trinity—Patrick stooped down and picked a leaf of shamrock. "See," he said, "these three green leaves are joined, yet grow from one stem; so surely are God the Father, God the Son, and God the Holy Ghost joined in one God."

And ever after this the little three-leaved shamrock became the chosen emblem of St Patrick.

Year after year Patrick toiled, bringing good where evil had been. Even the poisonous snakes were overcome by him, for, making a drum and taking two sticks, he went through the land beating his drum till his arms grew helpless with weariness. The snakes and serpents and all such deadly creatures fled before him, and at last were driven into the sea, never to return.

Folks say St Patrick lived till he was one hundred and twenty years old. He died on March 17 in his favourite resting-place, Dichu's Barn, where he had first said Mass in Ireland, and which was the place he loved above all others.

No candles were needed to burn beside him, for angels came to make the tomb bright with their presence, and thus Patrick, the Patron Saint of Ireland, passed with them into Paradise.

THE SNAKES AND SERPENTS FLED BEFORE HIM

VI

St Bridget

(ST BRIDGET's DAY: FEBRUARY 1)

JUST as the day was dawning on February the first, some fifteen hundred years ago, a little baby girl was born in Ireland. Her mother, a slave called Brotseack, was on her way home with a pitcher of warm milk, and as she crossed the threshold of the house, Bridget was born.

"Happy is the child that is born not in the house nor out of the house," they said. And the angels sprinkled the warm milk over the babe and christened her Bridget.

She grew up strong and healthy, and was fed from the milk of a snow-white cow set apart specially for her.

As soon as she was old enough she used to help tend the Druid's flocks on the moors and was very happy. Her lambs would follow her everywhere, and the wild birds grew quite tame and would let her stroke them.

The golden dandelion was her favourite flower, and the linnet seemed to sing its first song especially for her. She used to call it "The Little Bird of Bride."

New life sprang up wherever she went, and folk said of her, "She dips her fingers in the river, and the ice melts. She breathes upon the world, and winter is gone."

While quite young she prayed much to God, and once having found a little flat white stone, she said

A CHILD ANGEL CAME AND SET THE ALTAR UPON FOUR TINY FEET

it should be for her altar; but alas! she could not make it rest evenly on the ground, and was well-nigh giving up, when a child angel came and set the altar upon four tiny feet. Here Bridget used to pray each day.

She loved to share everything she had with others —her food, her toys, and even her clothes. No matter how many poor strangers came to the door, she would give them anything within reach, even when the things were not her own. This often led to trouble, but Bridget would pray earnestly, and the most wonderful things happened to help her.

As she churned, she would sing, "O God, bless my kitchen, that there may always be enough to give to those in need." She would half fill each jar with butter and say, "God will add something to it." And at her words each jar would become full.

About this time her father sent for her. He was rich, but not kind of heart, and soon grew tired of her strange ways; yet no words of his would make her cease giving to any beggar who came.

One day a grand dinner was prepared for his guests, and Bridget had just put the food upon the table when she heard a weary and faint whine, and, looking round, saw a half-starved dog gazing at her with pitiful, hungry eyes.

Bridget at once took a joint of meat from the table and gave it to the dog, which devoured it eagerly. Then, troubled at what she had done, Bridget covered her face with her hands in fear. Yet when she looked again, the joint was on the table as before and the dog was gone.

At last her father in anger took her off in a chariot to the King's castle, intending to sell her as a slave. When he went into the castle he left Bridget outside in the chariot. While she was waiting, a poor, ragged sick man came along and begged for money to buy food. Bridget's heart was full of pity and, having not a single coin, she looked round to see what she could give. Seeing her father's wonderful sword, a gift from the King himself, she put it into the beggar's hands, saying, "Go! Sell it, and buy food."

When the King and her father came out (the King being anxious to see what sort of a slave he was buying), she told him what she had done.

"O LORD, TAKE AWAY MY BEAUTY"

"My sword given to a beggar!" cried her father in a rage. "Well," said the King, "I cannot buy her, or all I possess will be given away. You had better marry her to anyone who will take her."

Now Bridget was very beautiful, and a young nobleman wanted to marry her, but she had no wish to belong to anyone save God. Her father, however, sent word to the nobleman and said she must obey his wish.

Then Bridget said to herself, "If my beauty were gone, no one would marry me." And she prayed, "O Lord, take away my beauty, then I can serve Thee alone."

And, strange to say, her face became changed, her golden hair lost its brightness, and her skin grew withered and unhealthy. At this the young nobleman no longer wanted her for his wife, and was glad to be rid of her.

Bridget then left her father's house and, with three other maidens, went to a holy Bishop. There she kneeled before the altar, and as he preached to them, he placed white robes upon them, and they promised to give up their lives to help the poor and needy.

"You shall be called Sisters of Mercy," said the Bishop, and as he spoke Bridget's beauty returned as of old, and even the wood of the altar-steps began to send forth fresh green shoots.

Bridget built for herself a hut or cell under the shelter of a mighty

"YOU SHALL BE CALLED SISTERS OF MERCY"

oak tree, and people called the place Kildare, the cell of the oak.

There she lived very simply. Once, when tending her cow, she let it feed on the grass near the roadside, for she had no land of her own.

"How much pasture do you need for your cow?" asked a rich man who was passing.

"As much as my cloak will cover," she answered.

"That you may have," he said.

So taking her cloak she spread it on the ground, but it grew so amazingly, that before long, miles and miles of Ireland were covered by the cloak, and she rejoiced that now she had more than enough for her needs.

Her life was happy beyond her dreams. To her also came many maidens all anxious to wear the white habit of her order, and to serve others as she was doing. Convents were built for them, and Bridget became the Abbess or Mother of them all.

Once a poor man chanced to kill a wolf near the King's palace, and thinking he would be rewarded, took it to the King. But the wolf happened to belong to the palace and was as gentle as a dog, and the man was therefore ordered to be put to death.

When Bridget heard of it she drove in her chariot towards the palace to plead for the man's life. As she went a huge wolf sprang from the woods and sat down quietly in the chariot beside her.

"You have been sent from Heaven," cried Bridget, and said to the King, "See! I have brought you a nobler wolf than the other. I pray you, pardon the poor man."

And the King could not but grant her wish.

Every one loved St Bridget. Even the sunbeams liked to be near her. One day an April shower came on, and, as she entered her cell, she flung her wet cloak over a sunbeam shining through the window, thinking it was a wooden beam.

The bright ray willingly held up the mantle hour after hour, but at last the sun set, and the sunbeam was anxious to be gone too. So it begged that Bridget would come and take her cloak.

She came quickly home and, lifting down her cloak, said, "I thank thee, gentle friend; but haste

SHE FLUNG HER WET CLOAK ON A SUNBEAM

away now, for the sun is set, and unless thou go fast thou wilt never come up with him!"

In an instant the sunbeam had vanished into the night.

So in the love of all things and beloved of all Ireland, St Bridget dwelt in her cell of the oak till she was seventy years old, when her glad spirit passed on to God.

VII

St Francis

(St Francis' Day: October 4)

ABOUT seven hundred years ago, in the town of
Assisi, in Italy, there lived a handsome, dark-eyed
boy called Francis. His father was a rich cloth-
merchant, and Francis grew up amid beautiful
things. He went to a school in a church on the
hillside, and when he became a young man he had
many friends among the rich people of Assisi.
He was fond of fine clothes and gay feasts and
songs and merriment, and was like the son of a
prince.

When he was twenty-five years old he became
very ill, and as he grew stronger he thought less
about his fine clothes and feasts, and decided to be
a soldier. Then one night he dreamed that he was
in a large room hung round with shining banners,
shields, spears, and daggers, and on each of these
he saw the Sign of the Cross.

As he stood wondering what it could mean, a
voice said, "These are the banners of Christ and
are for thee and thy knights."

Full of hope he set out to the war, but, as he
rode, it seemed that other voices were speaking to
him, bidding him to give up all for Christ, and at
last he cried, "What wouldst Thou have me to do,

O Lord?" And the answer came back, "Go to thine own land again."

So Francis left the soldiers and returned. His friend laughed at him, for he now laid aside all his rich clothes, and, giving them to a beggar, he dressed himself in the beggar's rags and sat down on the church steps, saying, "I will be poor as Christ Himself was poor. I will love poverty that I may help those in need more truly."

His father grew angry at his ways, and even shut him up for a time in a cellar; but when he was free he left his home for ever, saying, "I have no father now, but my Father in Heaven."

So, dressed in a coarse brown garment, with a rough cord round his waist and with bare feet, he went out among the people, preaching to them and nursing even the lepers. He lived on the poorest food, and men called him the Poor Little Man of Assisi.

One day, while he was praying in the little ruined church of St Damien, a voice said to him, "Francis, seest thou not that My House is in ruins? Go and restore it for Me."

"With good will, Lord," answered Francis.

And with his own hands he gathered together huge stones, carried them to the church, and there he began to build up the walls. At first people laughed at him and thought him mad, but before long they were filled with wonder, for the patient Francis toiled on till the whole church was restored.

In time others joined St Francis, and some

monks gave them a tiny church called the **Little Inheritance**, not far from Assisi. Here they lived in huts very simply, going out each day to preach

"FRANCIS, SEEST THOU NOT THAT MY HOUSE IS IN RUINS?"

and to help the sick, and they called one another Brothers.

In his journeyings Brother Francis made many friends. Everything and every creature he felt belonged to God's great family. The animals were his brothers and the birds his little sisters.

He would stop and talk to them, and they seemed

46

to understand all he said. Once he chanced to meet a young man taking some doves to be sold at the market.

"Give those gentle birds to me," he begged, "for they are holy and pure; do not kill them."

And the young man gave them to Brother Francis, who took them home and made nests for them, and they became so tame that they would eat from his hands without fear.

Another time he and his followers came to some great trees, and, looking up, Francis saw thousands of birds in the branches.

"Wait for me," he said. "I will go and preach to my little sisters, the birds."

The birds fluttered round him on the ground, and as he walked his rough robe brushed against them, yet they had no fear, but listened as he said:

"My little brothers and sisters, God is your loving Father. He has clothed you with feathers and has given you wings. He gives you food, and from the clear streams you can drink. You have high trees for your nests, and He cares for you. Then sing to Him, my little sisters, sing and praise Him for His great gifts to you."

The birds listened in silence, with bowed heads. Then they spread their wings and, opening their beaks, joined in a chorus of praise to God. Francis raised his hand and blessed them, saying, "Go in peace." And they rose like a great cross and, singing still, they flew off to north and south and east and west.

Once again, when Brother Francis was preaching to the people, the swallows were singing and chattering to one another so loudly that his voice could not be heard. Looking up to the birds, he said, "Be silent, my little sisters, that my people may

THEY ROSE LIKE A GREAT CROSS

hear my words." And immediately their singing and chattering ceased.

When Francis went to the town of Gubbio, he found the people in great distress, for a fierce wolf roamed in the forest near by and had carried off not only sheep and lambs, but little children also.

So Francis set out alone towards the forest. Soon he came near to the wolf's den, and as the creature sprang out as if to leap upon Francis, he made the Sign of the Cross and said, "Brother Wolf, come hither. I command you in the name of Christ to do no more harm to anyone."

48

Then the wolf came near and lay down at St Francis' feet, and he said, "Brother Wolf, you must make peace with the people of Gubbio and must promise never to torment them again, and they, in their turn, will always provide food for you."

"I COMMAND YOU IN THE NAME OF CHRIST"

The wolf wagged his tail and, lifting up his right paw, put it into St Francis' hand, as a sign that he had given his promise.

Then Francis led the wolf to the town, and in the market-place, where all the people were gathered, he said, "My brothers, will you promise to give food to Brother Wolf every day?"

And they answered, "We will, Brother Francis."

Then, turning to the wolf, he said, "And do you too promise to all this people to do them no harm?"

The wolf again put his paw into the hand of St Francis as a sign of his promise.

From that day the wolf lived among them, going from house to house like a dog, and being fed by them all.

Wherever he went, the people loved St Francis, and at last, when he became ill, they carried him back to the place he loved most, the Little Inheritance. There he grew weaker, and one day, when all the Brothers were gathered round him, he said,

"I pray you, my Brothers, most dear, that ye love one another."

Then, after blessing them all, he gave thanks to God for Brother Wind and Sister Water and Brother Fire and Sister Earth.

As the evening came, and the larks wheeled round about the hut where he lay, his face grew radiant with joy, for he loved the larks above all his little sisters.

So, as he lay listening to their evening hymn and watching them soar towards the heavens, his own beautiful soul passed on to God.

VIII

St Elizabeth

"I GIVE you joyous news," said a magician long ago to Herman, Landgrave of Thuringia. "I see a beautiful star rising over Hungary, and there, this night, is born a princess, who shall marry your son Louis, and in her shall many rejoice, for she will be a saint."

His words were indeed true, for on that night in November, 1207, Princess Elizabeth of Hungary was born.

Days and months passed by, and when the tiny princess was only four years old Herman (remembering the magician's words) asked that she might be allowed to live at his court in Thuringia with Louis, who was then eleven years old.

Great preparations were therefore made, and the princess dressed in beautiful robes of silk, embroidered in gold and silver, was placed in a cradle of gold and given to Count Walter of Varila, Herman's messenger.

Thirteen maids of honour were to go with the Princess, and the King sent also vast treasures of dresses and jewels and toys, and many costly gifts besides, for Herman and Lady Sophia, his wife.

There was great rejoicing when the procession

reached Thuringia, where the two children were betrothed and soon became happy playmates.

As she grew Elizabeth became very thoughtful and liked to go to church and pray. Sometimes she would say to her friends, "Let us race to the church." And if she won, she would slip inside alone and say a prayer. Or she would say, "Let us lie down and see who is the tallest." And in the quietness as they lay she would pray.

She was always giving away her toys, her clothes, and even her food, to the poor who came to beg at the castle gate.

When she had been there five years Herman died. Now Lady Sophia, and Agnes, her daughter, did not love Elizabeth as he had done, and they often made her feel very unhappy. They were haughty and selfish and could not understand her loving ways.

She liked to dress very humbly when she went to church, for she said, "Christ was poor, and we should set aside our jewels and rich robes when we pray to Him."

One day there was to be a grand festival at the church, and Lady Sophia ordered Elizabeth to put on her grandest garments and jewels and her golden coronet, and poor Elizabeth had to obey.

When, however, she came to the high altar she quietly set aside her crown, and bowed herself humbly in prayer. The Lady Sophia was angry, and on reaching home, said scornfully, "Why did you set aside your crown and act thus before all the people?"

"Dear lady, forgive me," answered Elizabeth, "but when I saw Christ on the Cross, crowned with thorns, I could not kneel before Him in my poor crown of gold and jewels."

Each day the Lady Sophia and her friends grew more unkind, but Louis loved Elizabeth dearly, and said, pointing to the highest peak of the mountains, "If that mountain were made of purest gold and set with jewels, I would not exchange it for Elizabeth. I love her more than anything on earth."

So the next year they were married amid great splendour, and were happy in each other's love.

As the time passed Elizabeth became more and more eager to help the poor, and was always ready to give anything she had.

On the day when Louis' sister Agnes was to be married, Elizabeth, dressed in a rich robe, over which was a beautiful bejewelled velvet cloak, was about to cross a courtyard leading to the banqueting-hall, when she saw a poor, ragged beggar half-starved and ill, lying upon the stones.

She had no time then to bring him food, but, hastily taking off her cloak, she gave it to the beggar. Then, remembering that none dared appear in the state hall without a cloak, she hurried back to her own apartments.

There in great haste came Louis to tell her that the banquet was ready and every one was waiting for her.

"I am ready, my lord," she said.

"But where is your mantle?" he said.

"I have given it away," she answered.

At that moment one of her maids entered, carrying the beautiful cloak on her arm. "My dear lady," she said, "is this not your cloak? I found it hanging in its place in the dressing-room."

HASTILY TAKING OFF HER CLOAK, SHE GAVE IT TO THE BEGGAR

Elizabeth drew the cloak round her, and, with a prayer of thanks to God, she went to the banquet, her garments shining as with a heavenly light. Then Louis knew that the ragged beggar was no other than the Christ Himself.

During the winter Elizabeth used to labour up and down steep snowy pathways many times to help those who were sick and needy and who dwelt at the foot of the crag. With her own hand she would carry heavy loads of bread and food for them.

One day, on one of these journeys, Louis met her and being grieved to find her so weary, said,

BEAUTIFUL RED AND WHITE ROSES

"Dear love, why do you carry so great a burden, and what is it you hold so closely in your mantle?"

Elizabeth in her humility tried to hide from him what it was, but he gently drew aside her cloak, and lo, her robe was no longer filled with food, but in its place were beautiful red and white roses, such as could only have grown in Paradise.

Louis gazed at her with awe, as at an angel, and

55

taking a red rose in his hand, he went on his way, and all his life he cherished the beautiful heavenly blossom.

For seven years Louis and Elizabeth and the three children born to them lived happily, caring nothing for Lady Sophia's unkindness. When famine and disease came upon the land, Elizabeth spent all her days in good works, feeding the hungry, caring for the sick, even selling the royal jewels to buy what was needed.

Then came the Crusades, and Louis felt called of God to set out to fight, but alas! he was smitten with fever and died before ever he reached the Holy Land.

Elizabeth's grief was terrible to behold.

"I have lost all," she cried. "The whole world is now dead for me." Indeed it seemed that all the world were against her, for with Louis she was safe, and now he was no longer there to protect her. She was banished with her children from the castle, and after wandering about in the snow, they found shelter in a mean dwelling in Marburg, where she was able to earn a little money by spinning wool.

But more terrible sufferings were to follow. Her children were taken from her, and she was made to act as a servant to those who were harsh and cruel to her.

Yet she bore all for Christ's sake, saying, "I have given up everything, my husband, my children, my riches, and my beauty. I give these to Him with all my heart."

56

Her frail body, however, grew weaker and weaker, till at last she could no longer rise from her bed, nor could her hand hold the distaff to spin, and with holy hymns upon her lips, her sweet life ended.

The magician's words were truly fulfilled—the little Princess was indeed a saint.

SHE WAS MADE TO ACT AS A SERVANT

IX
St Joan
(St Joan—May 30)

Jeanne d'Arc was born in the lovely little village of Domrémy, in 1412. Her father was a farmer, and Jeanne used to help him in the fields or with the cattle. She could not read or write, but her mother taught her to spin and sew as well as any lady in the land.

Jeanne spent many happy days playing with her friends in the meadows, but she would often steal away to church to pray while the others went to dance. She would nurse sick people, and many times let poor travellers sleep in her bed while she lay by the hearth all night.

She was a favourite with every one, and even birds and dumb animals would feed from her hands.

While still a child she learned that Charles the Dauphin, son of the French King, had been set on one side by some of the people—the Burgundians—and not allowed to be crowned King. The English, too, helped the Burgundians, and though the Orleanists remained faithful to the Dauphin, they had no great leader to fight for him.

One day Jeanne and her friends were running races. She ran so swiftly that her feet scarce seemed to touch the ground, and she easily won the race.

As she was resting at the far end of the meadow, some one seemed to appear and told her that her mother needed her. Hastening home, she found that her mother had not called her.

Jeanne was puzzled and was returning to her playmates when suddenly a bright cloud passed

A BRIGHT CLOUD PASSED BEFORE HER EYES

before her eyes, and a voice said that she must change her way of life and do wonderful deeds, for the King of Heaven had chosen her to help the Dauphin. She must wear man's dress, take up arms, and be a captain in the war, and all would obey her.

"But," said Jeanne, "I am only a peasant girl and cannot even ride a horse."

The voices came many times after that, and at last Jeanne felt she must obey them. So she persuaded her cousin to take her to the captain at

Vaucouleurs. But he only   ed at her story and said, "Box her ears and   ke her back to her father."

Jeanne, however, was not to be turned aside, and after many struggles she was allowed to set out for Chinon to see the Dauphin.

It was a dangerous journey with hardships, poor food, and little rest all the time; yet Jeanne was always cheerful, saying to her companions, "You must fear nothing, for God has sent me, and to Him all things are possible."

At last she reached the castle gates and was led into the Great Hall. They tried to deceive her by dressing one of the courtiers as the Dauphin, but she went straight to the true one and said, "Most noble Dauphin, I am sent by God to help you. My voices have warned me that I have but one year to live. Oh, send me, e'er it is too late!"

At last, after many delays, she was given an army and dressed in armour all of white, over which was a cloak of gold and velvet. She rode forth on a jet-black horse with a sword from the altar of St Catharine's Chapel. Her banner was of pure white, embroidered with lilies. On it was a figure of the King of Heaven bearing the world in his hand. Two angels were kneeling beside him, and below were written the words "Jesus Maria."

"Lead me to Orleans," said Jeanne, "and I will show you a sign, for I will raise the siege and crown the Dauphin."

So to Orleans they came, and there the battle

with the English was fierce and long; yet everywhere the Maid's white banner could be seen, as she fought on, cheering her soldiers as she cried, "Doubt not, the place is ours."

Once, when scaling a ladder against the walls, she was wounded and fell, but she was soon back

SHE RODE ON A JET-BLACK HORSE

again in her place. The English were amazed at her miraculous power and, thinking she must indeed be a witch, they became afraid and fled, leaving the peasant girl of seventeen victorious over her enemies.

Other battles followed, and, listening to and obeying her voices, she conquered everywhere; and on July 17, 1429, to her great joy, the Dauphin was crowned at Rheims Cathedral while Jeanne stood by his side, her white banner in her hand.

"Gentle King," she said, "now is accomplished the will of God. Let me return to Domrémy."

But the King would not hear of this, and bade her stay at the court, for he had need of her. Her life, however, from this time became troubled and unhappy, her voices came with less power, and in battle she was driven back. At last she was trapped and captured outside Compiègne by the Burgundians, and by them sold to the English.

She was imprisoned, and though she tried to escape was recaptured. Once she leaped down from a tower sixty feet in height, yet, as if by a miracle, she was not killed.

They took her to Rouen Castle, and placing her in a dark cell, chained her by hands, feet, and waist to a heavy log. For months she lay there suffering tortures both in mind and body, and then was led forth to be tried as a witch.

The trial lasted many days, and no matter how they tried to trap her, the brave Maid declared always that she had obeyed God.

"If you kill me," she cried, "I will say no other thing. I have done nothing against God and the Faith."

Yet, in spite of her innocence, she was sentenced to be burned in the market-place as a witch, and on May 31, 1431, she was led out to die.

Slowly she mounted the scaffold. As the crowd watched her, they wept, and even her enemies were moved to tears. Kneeling down, she prayed to the Holy Mary and all the saints and begged forgiveness for her sins. Then, turning to her judges, she said that she forgave them all the evil they had done her.

Before she was bound to the stake she asked for a cross. There was none to give her, but one of the English soldiers, in pity, broke his staff into two pieces and tied them together in the shape of a cross. This he gave her, and in joy she clasped it close to her breast.

As the fire mounted round her, the smoke rose and hid her from sight. Suddenly from the midst came her clear, ringing voice, strong in her faith as of old, saying, "My voices were of God. They have not deceived me."

Then, with the cry of "Jesu! Jesu!" upon her lips, the brave soul of the Maid of France passed to heaven.

"Alas," said one of the English soldiers, "we are lost, for we have burned a saint."

"ALAS—WE HAVE BURNED A SAINT"